Y0-DSO-739

MY FUN WITH
READING

♦

*Stories About
World Cultures*

MY FUN WITH READING

BOOK 3

Stories About World Cultures

SERIES EDITOR
Ronald Kidd

READING CONSULTANTS
Paul E. Stanton, Ph.D.
University of South Carolina, Coastal Carolina College

Ann Lukasevich, Ed.D.
University of British Columbia

THE SOUTHWESTERN COMPANY ■ NASHVILLE, TENNESSEE

RONALD KIDD is owner and Editorial Director of Kidd & Company, Inc., a Nashville-based packager and producer of children's books and records. Previously he held positions as Creative Director, Walt Disney Records, and Editor, Bowmar/Noble Publishers. The published author of seventeen books, he was recipient of the Children's Choice Award, the CINE Golden Eagle, and two Gold Records. He has been nominated for the Edgar Allan Poe Award, the Grammy Award, and the California Young Reader Medal. Mr. Kidd has a secondary teaching credential in English and history.

DR. PAUL E. STANTON completed his Ph.D. at the University of South Carolina in the field of Counseling Psychology, with an emphasis in reading and learning disabilities. He chaired the Department of Reading and Language Arts at the University of Pittsburgh and was co-chair of the Committee on Undergraduate Training in the Teaching of Reading for the International Reading Association (IRA). He was co-developer of the Scholastic *Action* Series, a pioneer high-interest/low-ability reading series produced by Scholastic Book Services. Dr. Stanton served as Vice Chancellor for Academic Affairs at the University of South Carolina, Coastal Carolina College, where he is currently Professor of Psychology specializing in reading and learning disabilities.

DR. ANN LUKASEVICH taught for seventeen years at the elementary school level in Ontario, Canada. She is presently a member of the Language Department at the University of British Columbia, where she originally obtained her Ed.D., and teaches courses in language, reading, early childhood, and curriculum development. She also taught reading and language courses at the University of Calgary for one year and at the University of Western Ontario for three years. During this period, she has done numerous workshops and conference presentations in early childhood education, reading, and language in Canada and the United States. She spent a year in Britain studying British education, and was awarded an advanced Diploma in Child Development. Her interests include parent involvement, evaluation, literacy development, and computer education.

SERIES DESIGN   Bruce Gore
PAGE DESIGN AND ART PRODUCTION   Schatz + Schatz
COVER PHOTOS   Stephen McBrady (top)
                 Yva Momatiuk and John Eastcott
                 (center and bottom)

Copyright © 1991
The Southwestern Company
Nashville, Tennessee

CONTENTS

Daughter of the Incas
page 7

Okhena Greets the Sun
page 37

The Water People
page 67

DAUGHTER
◀ *of the Incas* ▶

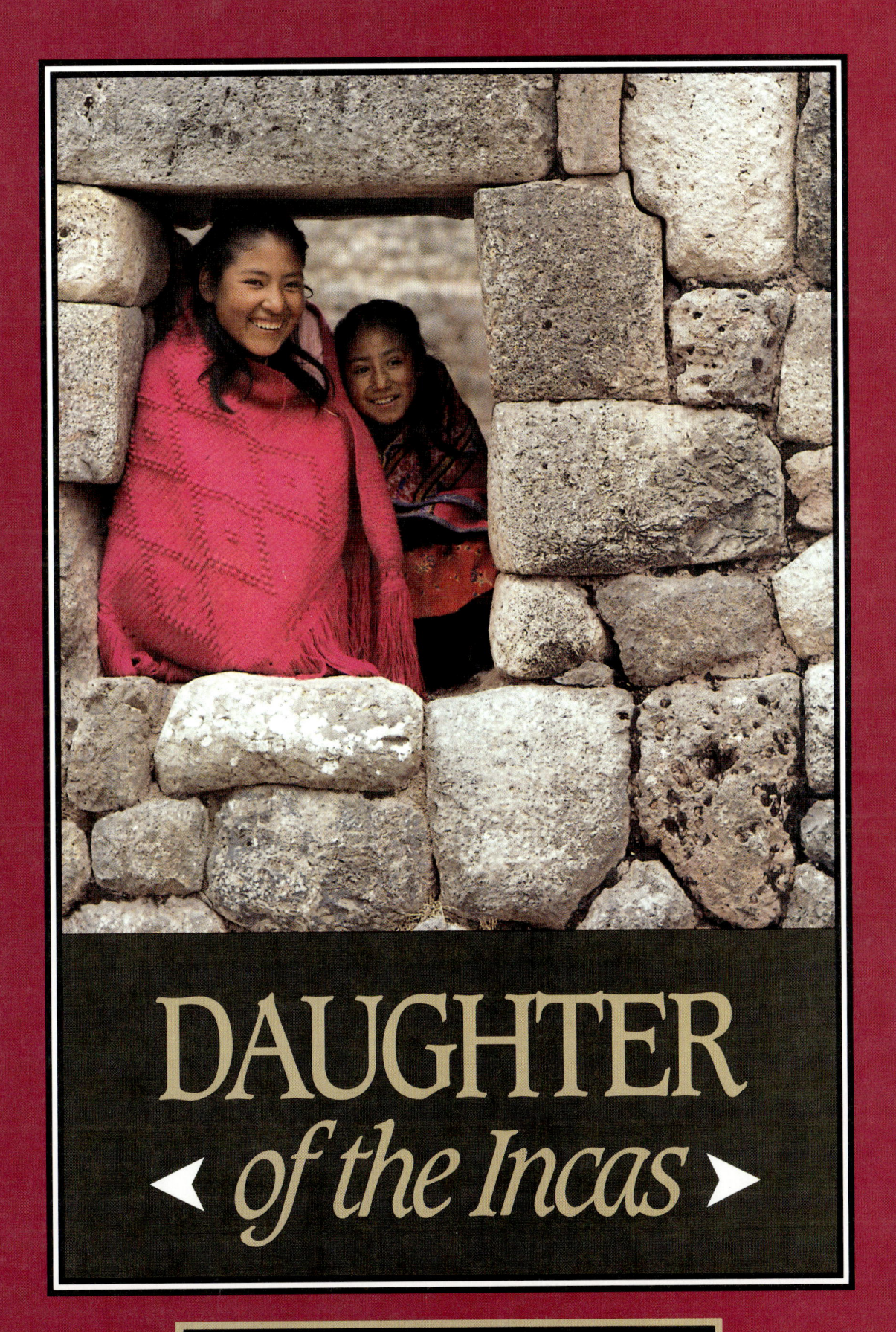

by STEPHEN McBRADY and RONALD KIDD

*If you need help
with hard words,
please turn to p. 36.*

PHOTOGRAPHS: Stephen McBrady
ILLUSTRATIONS: Joel Snyder

In a valley eleven thousand feet above the sea, a girl named Delia is picking quinua seeds. Quinua is a hardy plant that grows well in the thin, cool mountain air. Delia's family will use the seeds for making flour and thickening soups.

But this morning Delia is not thinking about flour or soups. Her mind is in another place, a place of mystery. She will be going there soon.

It is time.

Delia hurries across the fields to her house. Like the mountains themselves, the house is made of dirt and stone. Her big sister Estefa waits at the gate. Mariluz, her little sister, peeks out from behind. Her mother sits nearby, spinning yarn.

Delia's father brings his plow in from the fields. He changes clothes. Then he, Mariluz, and Delia walk down to the main road to wait for a bus to pass by.

Finally an old bus chugs up, and they climb on. It rattles off down the road. Delia gazes out the window and smiles. High peaks surround her village like the points of a crown. She never grows tired of looking at them.

Delia's village, or *pueblo,* is called Huancalle. It is in a valley high in the Andes Mountains of Peru. The area is sometimes called the Sacred Valley of the Incas, because it was the center of the ancient Inca Empire.

The Incas were a strong, proud people. They ruled the area from about 1200 to 1550. Their empire once stretched over two thousand miles, from Colombia in the north to Chile in the south.

The empire is gone, but the people are still here. Delia is one of them. She and her family speak Quechua, the language of the Incas. Except for her mother, they also speak Spanish.

The shaded area shows lands once ruled by the Incas.

All through this valley are ruins of the Inca Empire. From her seat on the bus, Delia is looking down at some of them. The ruins stretch along a mountain slope, far below the winding road. There are buildings whose roofs are long since gone. And there are great shelves, called *terraces,* dug out from the side of the mountain.

These terraces were used in farming. They made the soil level and kept it from washing away in the rain. The terraces were so well made that today they are still used by Delia's people.

The bus bumps along toward a town called Cuzco. It was the capital of the ancient Inca Empire. Outside of town, the bus stops. Delia, Mariluz, and their father get off.

They stand beside more Inca ruins. But these ruins are different. There are huge stone walls everywhere. The stones fit smoothly together like the pieces of a puzzle. Yet some of them are as big as trucks.

The Incas had no heavy, modern equipment. They had no motors. How did they move these stones? How did they pile them so high?

There is wonder in this place. Delia can feel it as she and Mariluz run to explore the ruins. The girls play hide-and-seek. Then they sit down on the steps of an ancient fortress, and their father tells them once more about the Incas.

Machu Picchu

Delia's favorite part is when he describes the ruins of Machu Picchu. Perched on a peak in the

Andes, this mysterious city was forgotten for years, then discovered again in 1911.

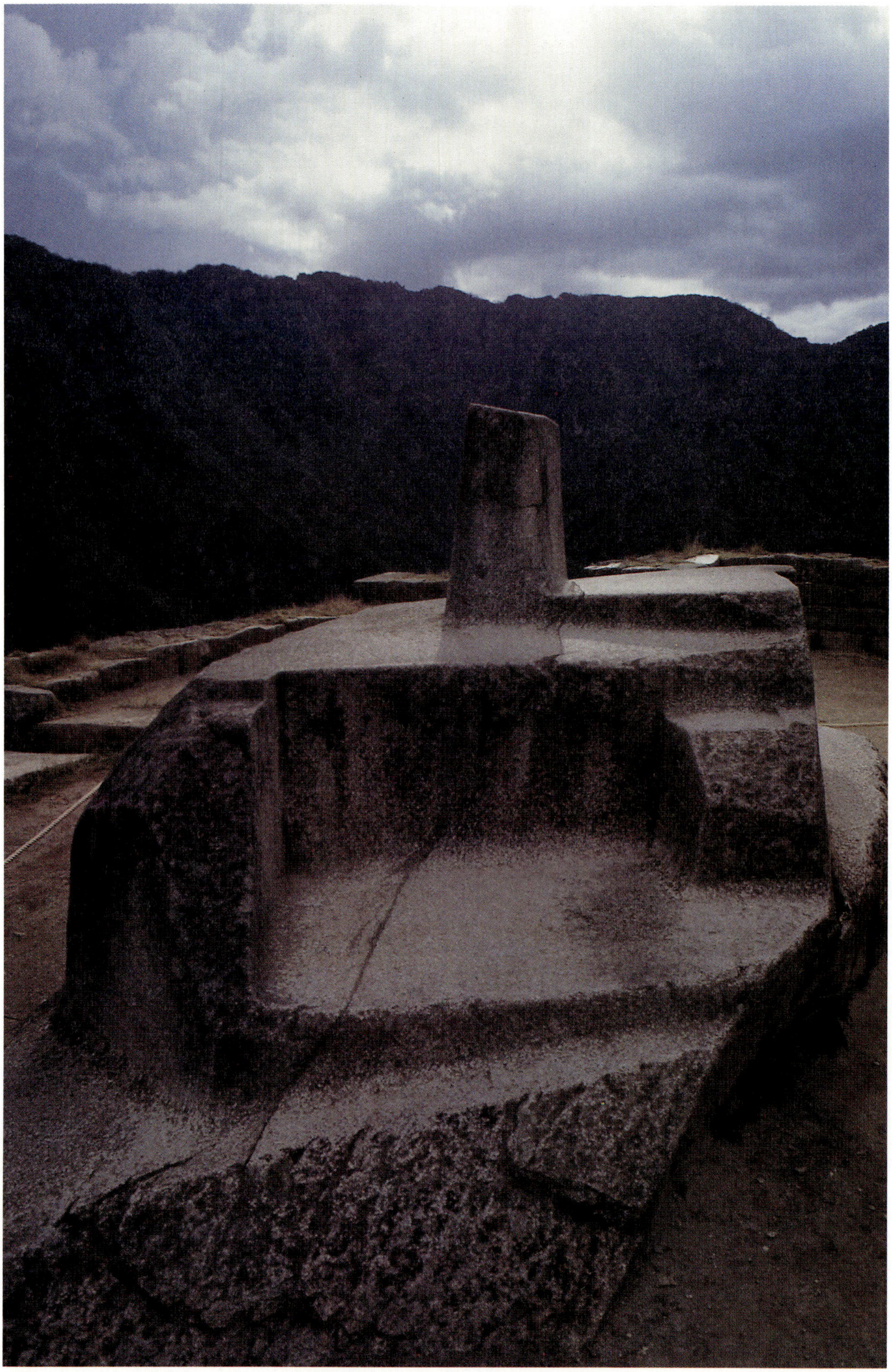

At Machu Picchu is the famous Inti Huatana, or "hitching post of the sun." Some say it was used by Inca astronomers to predict how long the days would be. Delia dreams of going there to see it someday.

In the meantime, there are other dreams and other duties. When the sun dips low in the sky, Delia and her father and sister head back home. On Monday morning the week begins once again.

Inti Huatana

Delia is up at five o'clock. While she gets dressed, her mother milks their three cows. Delia drinks a glass of this milk for breakfast, along with some cheese her mother has made and a potato. Then she sets out for school.

Delia and the other children of her pueblo go to school in Pisac, over six miles down a very steep mountain trail. The walk takes 2½ hours. Last year Delia slipped on the mountain path and cut her leg on a stone. Her friends helped her up to the road and stopped a car to take her home. Delia's mother put herbs on the leg.

Delia likes arriving at school early. She talks with her friends about homework. When school starts, she has six classes: math, science, history, civics, geography, and religion. Delia likes math and science best. There are two recess periods, when she plays games or does her studies. Delia works hard, because she wants to be a teacher.

School is over at one o'clock. Since the trip home is a hard climb, it takes over three hours. By the end, Delia's feet seem as heavy as Inca stones. They feel lighter, though, when she sees Mariluz and the dogs waiting for her by the gate.

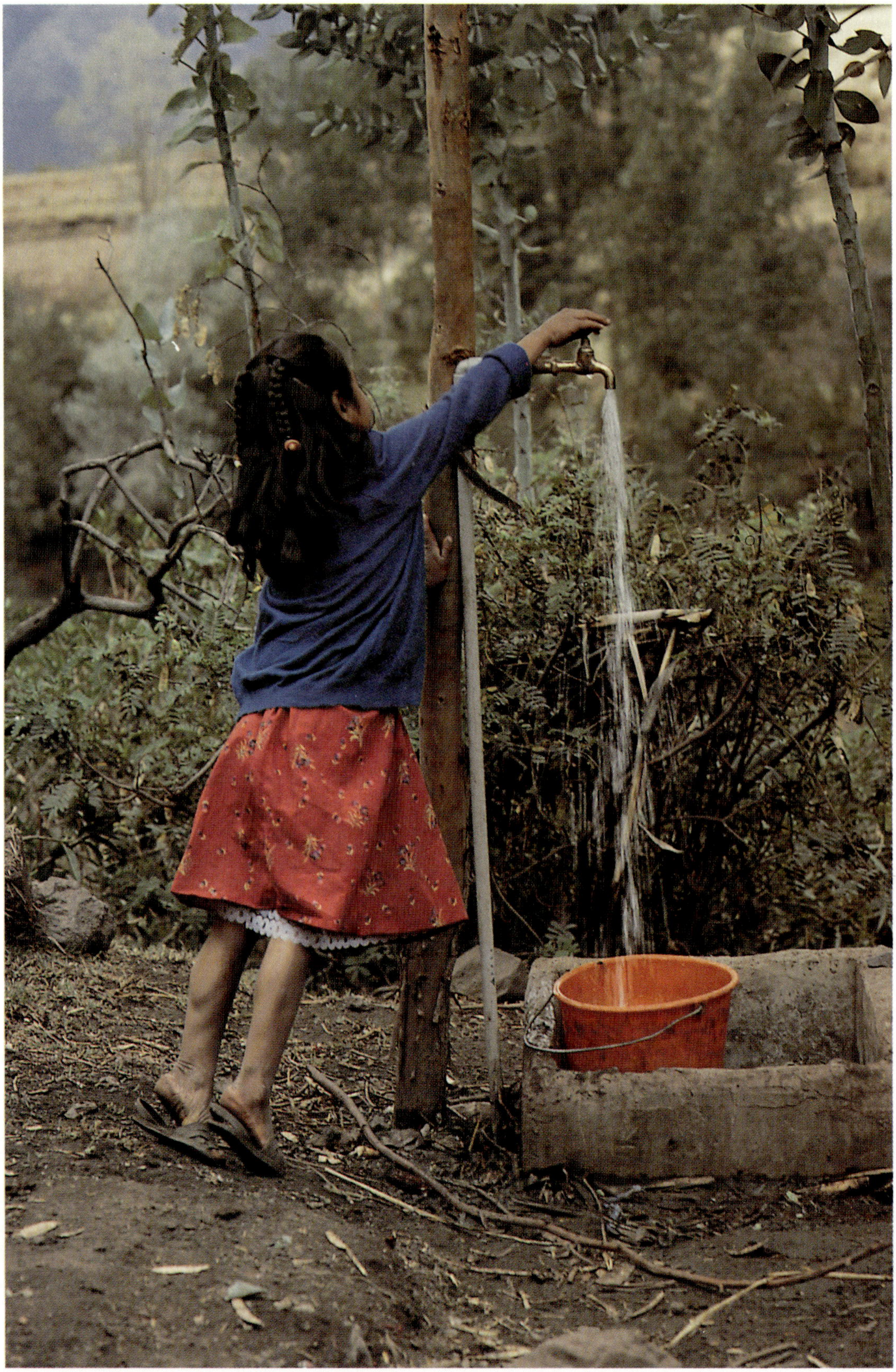

As Delia changes clothes, Mariluz goes to get water. There is a faucet outside, connected by pipes to a lake called a *reservoir,* high above the pueblo.

When it's time to water the fields, the reservoir is not full enough for the faucets to work. Then someone in the family must walk up the mountain to get two buckets of water. The trip takes three hours. Mariluz is glad that today the faucet is working.

While her sister is outside, Delia begins to cook supper for the family. She often makes vegetable soup, using the many different plants her father grows on their land.

One room of the house is used for storing food, and this is where Delia goes first. The potato is the chief food, as it was for the Incas. There are many kinds of potato, with different sizes, shapes, colors, and flavors. The "papa amarilla," with its nutlike taste, is Delia's favorite. Besides potatoes, Delia's father grows quinua, corn, cabbage, squash, beans, and many other plants and herbs.

Delia gathers the vegetables into a bowl. Then she moves into the kitchen, where an open fire is burning. As she cooks, there are squeaking noises from the corner of the kitchen. She throws a cabbage leaf to quiet the *cuyes,* which are a kind of guinea pig. Since the ancient days of the Incas, cuyes have provided a good source of meat. Delia's family also raises chickens, pigs, and lamb.

After supper, Delia does her homework. If there is time she likes to watch the small black-and-white TV set. Since the house has no electricity, the set is powered from a car battery. When the battery power gets too low to run the TV, it is used to play the radio. Then every couple of months, Delia's father takes the battery to be charged.

On days when there is no school, Delia and her father sometimes travel to the colorful open-air market in Pisac. They might buy some bread, salt, matches, or shoes.

They sell vegetables the family has raised and clothing they have made.

A shoemaker

When Delia gets home, she takes a few minutes to relax. During these happy times she and the other children might jump rope or play jacks. She might just sit and talk with her parents.

DAUGHTER OF THE INCAS   33

On most Saturdays Delia herds the cows and sheep. She and Mariluz take them eight miles up the mountain, where there are good pastures. For lunch the girls eat *charqui.* This is the Quechua word for dried meat. It's where our word *jerky* comes from.

Delia likes herding the sheep, because there is not much to do. She can sit curled up to keep warm as she knits clothes. She thinks about school and the things she sees on TV. But mostly, her mind drifts off to the high places and the old times when Incas ruled the land.

Mystery was in these mountains. It still is.

What Does It Mean?

empire: lands ruled by a strong leader

equipment: tools

hardy: strong

herbs: plants used as medicine

hitching post: a pole to which horses or other animals are tied

predict: to tell or guess what is to come

surround: to close in on all sides

How Do You Say It?

charqui: CHAR kee

cuyes: KOO yays

Cuzco: KOOZ coe

Delia: DAY lee uh

Estefa: es TAY fah

Huancalle: whang kah YAY

Inti Huatana: een tee hua TAH nah

Machu Picchu: mah chu PEE chu

Mariluz: mah ree LOOS

Pisac: PEE sock

Quechua: KAYTCH wah

Okhena
GREETS THE SUN

by YVA MOMATIUK and JOHN EASTCOTT

*If you need help
with hard words,
please turn to p. 66.*

PHOTOGRAPHS: Yva Momatiuk and John Eastcott
ILLUSTRATIONS: Joel Snyder

T here is a whisper in the night. "Wake up, wake up."

Ten-year-old Okhena stirs in his sleeping bag. He hears someone slipping out of the tent.

Who woke him? Okhena's younger brothers are asleep. His father always comes and goes as silently as a cloud spirit. It must have been his older brother, Tikhak.

A freezing Arctic wind twirls inside the tent. Okhena pokes his head outside. A ground squirrel peers at him in the soft yellow light. It is now June, and midnight, but the golden sun rolls above the horizon like a fiery soccer ball. It will not set until August.

He looks around. If Tikhak's rifle has moved from its usual spot, he is going somewhere. The wind may break the thinning sea ice, making sled travel dangerous. But the rifle is gone, and so are the dogs.

Arctic ground squirrel, called hikhik

Okhena panics. Once before, he missed a chance to join his brother on a trip. That time Tikhak returned triumphant, pulling the body of a ringed seal behind him. The family ate some. The rest was stored under icy rocks for use later.

Okhena's brother Tikhak returned pulling the body of a ringed seal behind him.

A team of husky sled dogs basks in the evening sun beside Okhena's family camp.

Barefoot, Okhena runs down the beach. He nearly stumbles over Tikhak's sled. His big brother looks at Okhena's red toes, grins, and starts to harness the barking dogs.

Tikhak does not ask if Okhena wants to go; he sees that his little brother is dying to join him. And Okhena does not ask if he can come; Tikhak's grin tells Okhena that his brother will wait for him.

Tikhak and Okhena are Inuit. The word means "real people" in their Inuktitut language. They are also known as Eskimos. This is an Indian word meaning "eaters of raw meat." But they do not like this name.

In the Inuit culture, questions are thought to be unnecessary and even rude. When asked something, people might say, *"Atchoo."* This roughly means: "Don't ask me. I don't know any

Okhena says "yes" and "no" in the body language of the Inuit.

better than you do. Besides, you can guess the answer if you have been watching." Instead of using questions, the Inuit learn by looking for clues, as if they were detectives.

*Inuit have snowmobiles
but trust their huskies more.
"Dogs don't break down or
stall while going uphill,"
they say.*

Okhena runs back to the tent. He dresses and grabs his fur-rimmed parka. Then he yells at the dogs to move and hops on the sled behind Tikhak.

The loaded sled glides onto the highway of the frozen sea. The ice is getting mushy during the day. But it refreezes when the night comes.

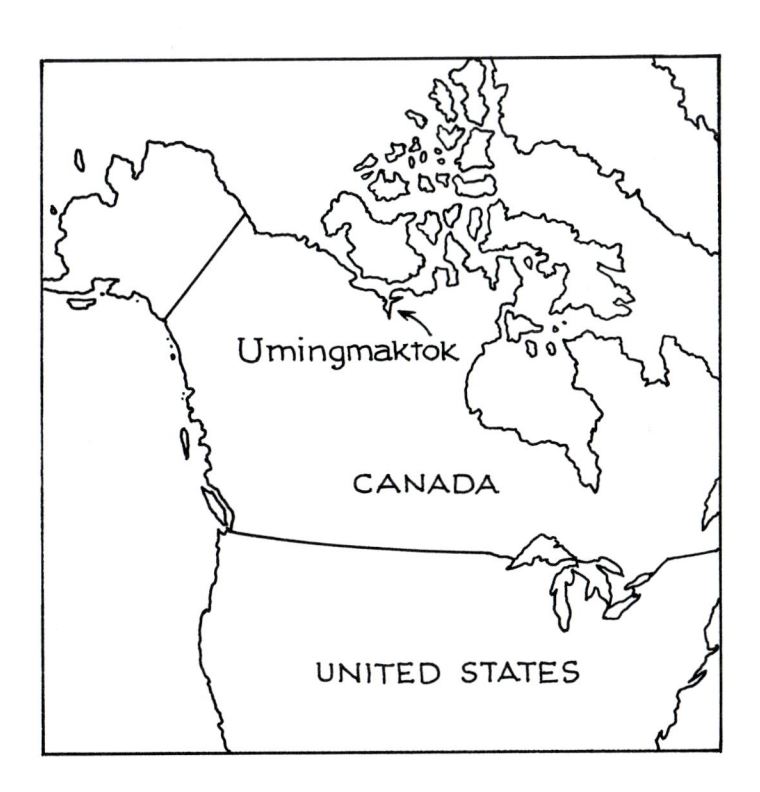

All winter long Okhena waited for the sun. He and his family spent those months in their one-room house in the tiny village of Umingmaktok (Place Where the Muskoxen Are Many). Theirs was

Endangered and now protected, the muskoxen can be hunted only by the Inuit, who eat the meat and use the horns for making fishing spears and knife handles.

the only town in Canada's Arctic with no *kablunat* (white people). There were no roads, no television, no church, and no school. The store ran out of goods in January. But the Umingmaktormiuts liked to live by themselves. They got much of their food from the land and sea around them.

Sometimes they visited their relatives in distant Arctic towns. They giggled at television shows. They sampled fried chicken and rode in the back of pickups bounding on rough town roads. But they did not want to move there. Too boring, they said.

Okhena's father uses his binoculars to spot distant caribou.

In winter they did not see the sun for four months. On many days the cold reached forty degrees below zero. The wind whipped snow into stinging darts.

This caribou is well camouflaged among the rocks.

*Okhena's mother and aunt
cut caribou meat
into narrow strips and
hang them to dry next
to the fish.*

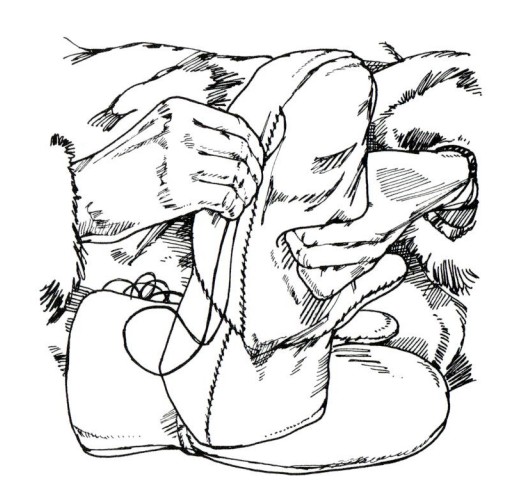

52   OKHENA GREETS THE SUN

This was a lazy time of long naps and longer stories. The tales were of spirits and animals with special powers, told in a low voice by Okhena's grandmother. Okhena listened, munching on *mipku,* dried caribou meat.

The boy loved the stories but longed to be outside. He dreamed of turning into a gray wolf and roaming the frozen world.

Okhena's cousins play "caribou" on the rocks.

One day last March the sun rolled out and Okhena's parents got busy. They sewed new clothes for the family and ice booties for the sled dogs. They made rounded *ulu* knives. They repaired the old outboard motor for their boat. Early in June the family moved to its summer camp, forty miles from Umingmaktok. Pitching a tent, they waited for good weather.

Warmer days invite travel. Okhena's uncle, aunt, and cousins come sixty miles across the sea just to visit.

The good weather has come, and Okhena is thrilled. He and his brother have been speeding across the ice for several hours now. The boy is as excited as the dogs, who are running and growling at each other.

Okhena's cousin tenderly holds her younger sister.

Okhena plays his own game of ice hockey.

Soon he feels tired. On the moving sled, Okhena crawls under a caribou skin and falls asleep. When he wakes up, the sled stands still. A pot of brown-spotted eggs is boiling on an old stove on the beach.

As his father watches, Okhena tries on a new pair of blue jeans that just arrived at the village store.

Okhena's sister opens her new music box, ordered by catalog a year ago.

Tikhak must have found seagull nests. Okhena's mouth twists with hunger. Gratefully he pulls out a hot egg and eats it, savoring each bite. Its yolk is huge. It seems to smile at him, so he smiles back pleasantly.

Instead of a car, the Umingmaktok store has one wheelbarrow. Okhena takes his cousin on a ride across the tundra.

Okhena loves flying his new kite high on the rocks.

All around him the snow is melting into bubbling rivulets. Thousands of birds honk from the cliff. The sun is so hot he strips off his parka. He begins to run in big circles, his fingers touching the ground. Now he is a sled dog, now a caribou, now a wolverine! He chants:

> *There is a joy*
> *in feeling the warmth*
> *come to the great world*
> *and seeing the sun*
> *follow its old footprints*
> *in the summer night.*
> *Y-aaa, Y-aaa, Y-a…*

The joys of summer include playing with new sled dog puppies.

He throws himself on a bed of orange lichens and breathes deeply. But where is Tikhak?

Okhena gets up and heads toward the sound of rushing water. This is Ekalulia, a river full of glistening Arctic char fish. And there is Tikhak in the middle of the river. He is jumping over boulders, his fishing spear flashing in the sun.

So many fish! Tikhak must have worked hard all morning, while Okhena slept like a log. Since you can only count to five in Inuktitut, Okhena thinks there are as many fish as there are fingers and toes of three people.

Okhena's small sister finds these tasty seagull eggs all by herself.

Holding his spear ready, Tikhak looks for Arctic char fish in the Ekalulia River.

OKHENA GREETS THE SUN

He helps Tikhak carry the shiny bodies, feeling their precious weight. His mother and sisters will clean the fish. Then they will dry the meat for the long winter ahead. No vegetables, grain, or fruit can be grown in the tundra where Okhena lives.

The sun-dried char meat decorates wooden racks near Okhena's tent.

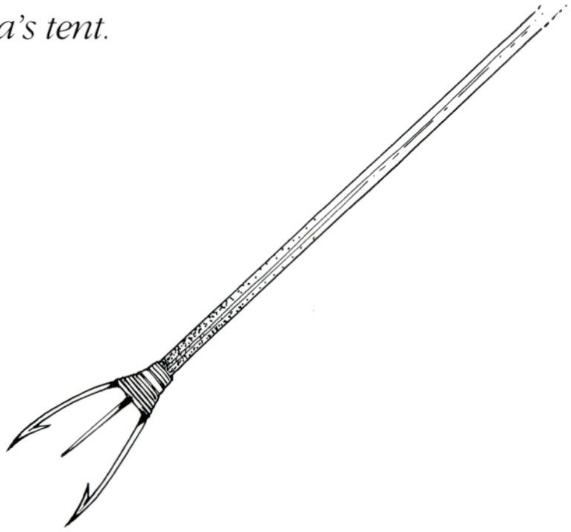

Okhena loads the freshly caught char into a caribou skin bag.

His family eats meat and fish. Seal flippers, caribou tongues, and bone marrow are highly prized. But most of all, Okhena loves the crunchy fish eyeballs.

Dry char is tasty but chewy. Okhena's cousin cuts off each bite with a sharp pocket knife.

Imitating her mother, Okhena's sister cuts up her first char with a small ulu *knife.*

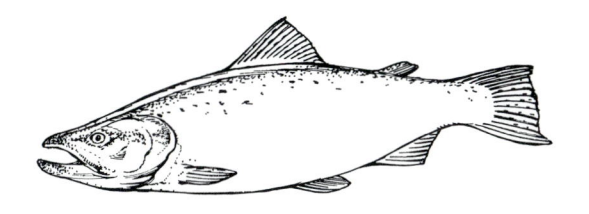

Arctic char fish

OKHENA GREETS THE SUN

The trip back to camp is long. Okhena knows whining will not make it shorter. The day is hot, and the ice has begun to melt. The boys use their sled as a bridge across the cracks. When they get home, Okhena dives inside the tent and gulps down a bellyful of tea. It is midnight again.

That day is the start of summer for him. Warm days bring mosquitoes. But they also bring swims in the creeks, trips to the store, visits to the camps of other Inuit families, and hours of play.

During spring trips Okhena and his family often use their sled to bridge cracks in the sea ice, then carefully crawl across.

For the Inuit, there is no better drink than tea made from melted ice water. In the summer Okhena's uncle travels by boat to find a good patch of ice.

His mother, Tonokahak, spends her days carving soapstone figures. These she sells. She never chases him off to bed. She knows that when he gets tired, he will crawl into his sleeping bag.

No one scolds him or tells him no. The Inuit feel that children learn not by *do*s and *don't*s, but by imitating those they admire most, often an older brother or sister.

Fall comes. The tundra brightens with red and orange hues. Berries ripen and burst on Okhena's tongue, filling his mouth with sweet and tart juices.

Okhena's parents make soapstone carvings to help pay for supplies.

One evening he wanders away from the camp to inspect *inukshooks*. These are man-like stone figures on a nearby ridge. They were built by his ancestors.

Okhena rounds a rocky outcrop and freezes. There, staring him in the face, stands a large gray wolf. Surprised, the boy and the animal barely breathe. Suddenly the wolf takes a deep whiff of Okhena's scent and is gone.

Okhena and his sister play among the inukshooks.

The boy does not run away or call for help. He thinks of a story told by his grandmother. There are certain animals, she said, that never attack human children. These animals have lost their brothers and sisters. They feel sad and desperately try to find new ones. They are kind but very, very shy.

"Just like my wolf," thinks Okhena. "I think he wants me for a brother."

Okhena walks slowly back to the tent. He bundles up in his sleeping bag. Closing his eyes, he says quietly, "I have a new brother, the wolf."

And he sleeps.

What Does It Mean?

ancestors: relatives of long ago

Arctic: the area around the North Pole

harness: to tie together for pulling

lichen: a kind of plant that grows on rocks

marrow: matter found inside the bone

parka: a heavy coat with a hood

soapstone: a soft grey or green stone

tundra: a flat plain in the far north

How Do You Say It?

Ekalulia: eck ah LOO lee ah

Inuit: IN oo it

inukshooks: ih NOOK shooks

Inuktitut: in OOK tih toot

kablunat: kah BLOO naht

Okhena: o KEH nah

Tikhak: TEEK hahk

Tonokahak: toe noe KAH hahk

Umingmaktok: oo ming MAHK took

Umingmaktormiuts: oo ming MAHK tor mee oots

The Water People

by YVA MOMATIUK and JOHN EASTCOTT

*If you need help
with hard words,
please turn to p. 96.*

PHOTOGRAPHS: John Eastcott and Yva Momatiuk
ILLUSTRATIONS: Joel Snyder
AUTHORS' DEDICATION: To Zhao, who introduced us to the Tai people.

Perched on the back of her family's water buffalo, Yi Bo starts to laugh. The animal is snorting so loudly she cannot help it.

Yi Bo urges the buffalo on, tapping its sides with her bare feet and waving her stick. The animal obediently plows into the river. Now only its nostrils stick out above the current, like funny bullfrogs. Yi Bo laughs again.

Yi Bo (left) *and friend graze their water buffalo along a road leading out of Mangsha.*

The family water buffalo swims in the river.

    She is glad she came to the river. Its murky current flows past the rice paddies just behind Mangsha, Yi Bo's village. Everything is so green here. Each moving bamboo stalk seems to whisper a different song.

The June morning is already hot and humid. But the river, which flows from the grasshopper-green mountains rimming the valley, is deliciously cool.

Yi Bo is not alone. On the river bank she sees other buffalo grazing. Nearby, children swim in the gurgling rapids. Women wash clothes, graceful in their tight blouses and flowery skirts. From between their lips come flashes of gold.

Village people swim, wash, and play while water buffalo are tied to their poles nearby.

THE WATER PEOPLE

"When I grow up, I'll go to the market and see the man called Dentist," dreams Yi Bo. "I'll ask him to cover my teeth with gold. Then I can look rich and beautiful, too."

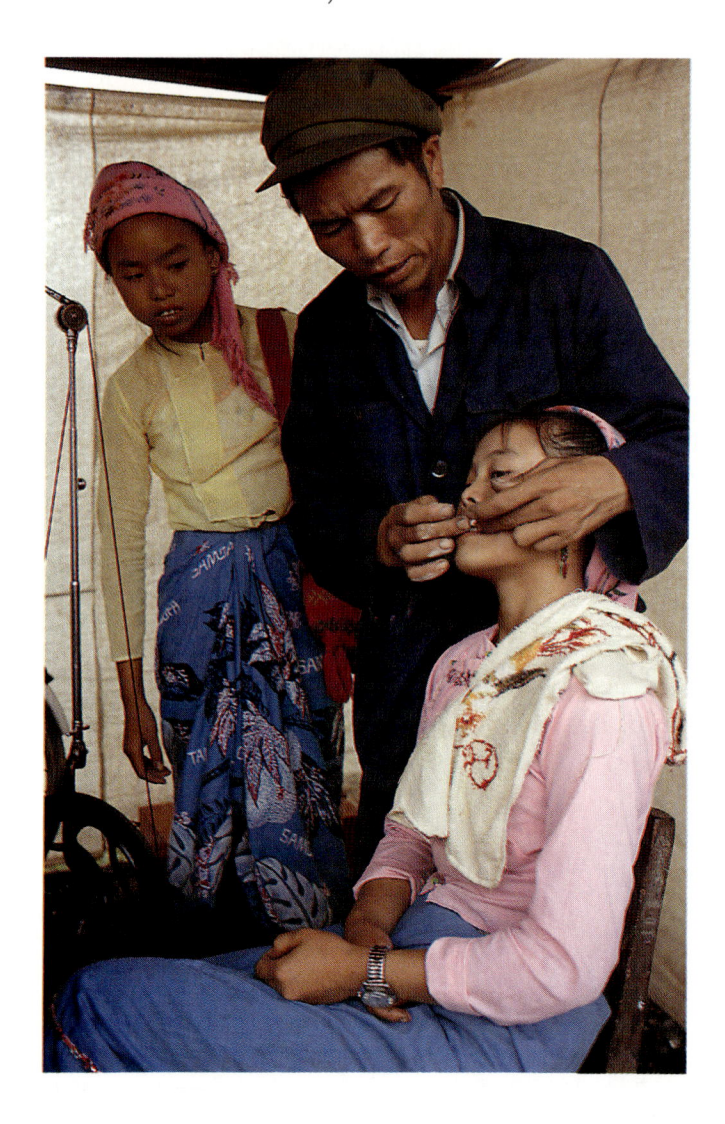

The village dentist puts a gold crown on a young woman's tooth.

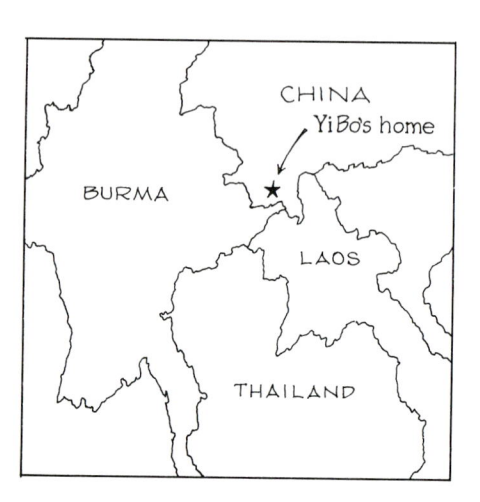

THE WATER PEOPLE

An old man watches the rice fields outside Mangsha.

Yi Bo lives in China, a country with more than one billion people. But she and her family are not Chinese. They are Tai. Since much of their work and play centers around ponds and a river, they are sometimes called "water people." There are about 760,000 Tai. All of them live in the province of Yunnan, in the south of China.

There are many butterflies in the forests near town.

They wear traditional Tai clothes and have their own holidays and customs. They are a small, separate group of people, called a *minority*. There are fifty-five different minorities in China.

The mountainous area where the Tai live is a lush kingdom of plants, always warm. Trees spread their huge leaves, shaped like umbrellas and bird wings. Butterflies are everywhere. Some flowers are as big as wash basins.

There are only two seasons here: dry, from November till April, and wet during the rest of the year. Wet seasons are caused by monsoons, strong winds blowing from the far-away ocean. They bring heavy rains. Without monsoons, the rice and tea plants and the great fruit-bearing trees would die.

Yi Bo is afraid of the tigers and boa constrictors which live deep in the forest. But she would like to see the peacocks, monkeys, and especially deer.

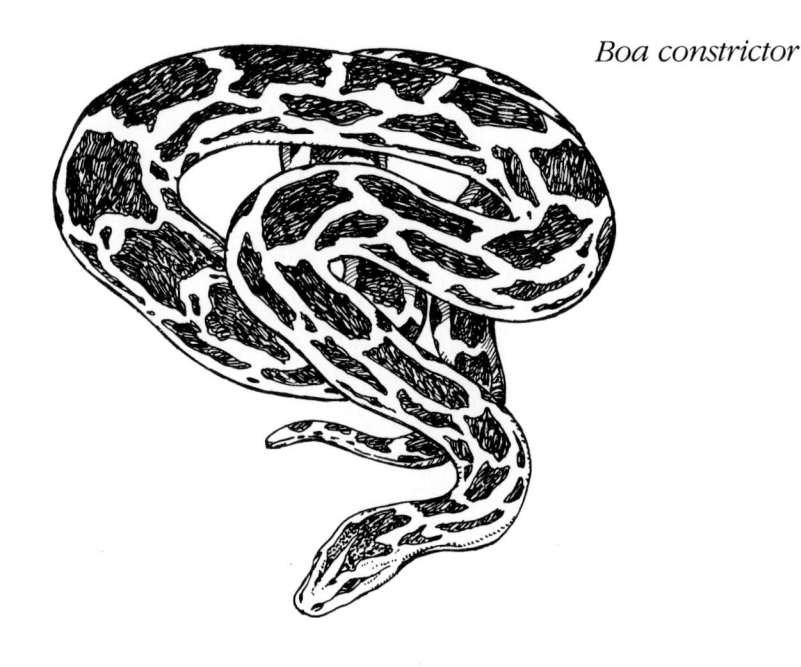

Boa constrictor

The job of tending the animals is shared by everyone in the village.

Her mother told her the land of the Tai was discovered thousands of years ago by hunters chasing a golden deer. It led them over seventy-seven emerald peaks and ninety-nine blue rivers until they came upon a golden lake. The animal leaped in and disappeared. Enchanted, the young hunters settled around the lake with their families. If only she could find that deer....

Loud splashes wake Yi Bo from her dream. Some boys are swimming toward her. Yi Bo, who is only eight, feels uneasy. They may pull her off the water buffalo and dunk her. One boy is already holding its tail. Without looking, she slaps him with her stick.

Ai Un (left) *plays with a friend in the river.*

Water buffalo

THE WATER PEOPLE 77

"Hey, it's your brother you are hitting, you feisty bird," he says. It is Ai Un, her ten-year-old brother.

He looks at her closely. "Were you scared?" he asks. Yi Bo admits she was, but says she is fine now.

Ai Un after a swim

The temple at the Buddhist monastery on top of the hill

She is never afraid when he is around. But last winter Ai Un and other boys left their cozy bamboo houses in the village. They moved to the big Buddhist monastery at the top of the hill.

There was a great ceremony. Families and guests ate ground beef with spices, and puffed rice mixed with brown sugar. People carried "money trees." These were decorated with things the boys might need, such as toothbrushes, and money for the monks. Yi Bo still remembers the fireworks exploding against the dark sky.

After that night, Ai Un began his studies at the monastery. He also received a new name. It is Ai Mai Un, *mai* meaning "new." One day he may take holy vows and become a monk. He often visits his family during the day. But at night he must return to the monastery.

Aini woman

"I came yesterday, but you were not home," says Ai Mai Un.

"Mother and I went to the big market on the other side of the river," she explains excitedly. "I saw women who wore silver coins and green beetles. Mother said they are called Aini and come from a village deep in the forest. I couldn't stop looking at them, so I kept tripping."

"That's what happens to all curious girls," says Ai Mai Un. "We boys never look around."

They both laugh so hard that Yi Bo loses her balance and slips into the river. She pulls Ai Mai Un after her.

Ornament made of green beetles

Mangsha's narrow streets are full of people and animals.

    Wet and happy, the children take their animal back to the village. They tie him under their small bamboo house. Like all houses in Mangsha, it is built on high stilts. It has a living room, one bedroom, and a sunny porch. But the house is empty.

Yi Bo comes out of the river.

THE WATER PEOPLE

Where are their parents? The children walk down the dusty street. They wave at their uncles building a new house and shout at friends playing with sling shots. They laugh at the man selling drinks. He has fallen asleep.

Carpenters building a roof on a new house

A boy plays with his sling shot as other children watch.

The cold drink seller

The children nearly bump into their grandfather, who stands in the middle of the path. And here is their cousin, Yi Tan! She carries her fat baby brother. Yi Bo gives him some water from a folded tree leaf.

Yi Bo's grandfather

Yi Bo gives a drink of water to Yi Tan's baby brother.

Around the corner, an old man is turning tea leaves with his feet to dry the leaves faster. Ai Mai Un greets him respectfully. The man asks, "Will you become a monk and grow up to be a man of wisdom?"

"Maybe," replies Ai Mai Un. "If I work hard and our parents can pay for my studies. Or maybe I'll go home and look for a wife, a girl as nice as my sister." Yi Bo likes that.

They find their parents by the village ponds.

An old man turns tea leaves with his feet.

Father is fishing. The children help him, beating the water with sticks to drive fish into his net. Out on another pond, two women bob on a tire tube, gathering water chestnuts. They paddle to the edge of the pond, lift their heavy bundles of chestnuts, and nimbly jump to the shore.

Two women gather water chestnuts.

Yi Bo's mother carefully washes the family water buffalo.

Yi Bo's father is fishing.

Mountain mists rising after afternoon monsoon rainstorm

Yi Bo no longer knows if she wants to be rich and beautiful, or strong and independent, like these women. Maybe both?

A quick shower falls from the monsoon clouds above. The valley fills with light mist. It is getting dark, and Ai Mai Un must return to the monastery.

A rainbow above the monastery

    The children hurry up the path, hand in hand. Yi Bo thinks that in his new robe, Ai Mai Un looks older, wiser. But she misses him.

    "Why does he want to live in that old place?" she mutters to herself. He is her best friend, and she does not want to lose him.

Yet she knows that many Tai parents who can afford it send their sons to monasteries. The boys learn about Buddhism, the religion of the Tai. They read the *sutras,* sacred texts written in an old Tai script. She also knows that as the youngest child, she will be expected to live with her parents until they die, and she's proud.

Ai Mai Un (far right) *helps to light candles in front of the altar to Buddha.*

Traditional drum

Ai Mai Un tells her that each morning he chants and prays in the temple. Later he sweeps the monastery with the other boys. He practices playing an elephant foot drum, used during religious ceremonies. He has lessons. Even if he does not become a monk, people will always respect him for what he knows.

Every morning, Ai Mai Un and the others sweep the monastery with bamboo brooms.

Playing elephant foot drums during religious ceremonies at the temple

THE WATER PEOPLE

Walking to class

"The monks teach me stories about the past," says Ai Mai Un. "They show me how to draw, paint, and sculpt. When I get older, I'll also learn how to cure sick people. I'll study the sky, too."

"Do you watch the stars?" asks Yi Bo.

"Yes, especially the big pink one you like so much," he says. "I think about you, and also about Mother and Father. They must raise many pigs and chickens to pay for my studies. Do you know that parents who send their sons to the

Ai Mai Un and friend look over Mangsha's rice fields and green hills beyond.

monastery receive gold stars for their effort? When they die, these stars will erase what they did wrong during their lives."

"Mother and Father never did anything wrong," says Yi Bo.

Her brother puts his arms around her. "We all do. Don't you?"

"Not when you are around," Yi Bo answers.

Thinking about Ai Mai Un watching the same stars in the black silk of the night, she feels good.

What Does It Mean?

bamboo: a woody plant that is often hollow inside

boa constrictor: a large brown snake that kills by squeezing

monastery: a place where monks live

saffron-colored: a deep orange-yellow

stilts: long poles used to hold something above the ground or out of the water

vendor: someone who sells things

water buffalo: a slow, oxlike animal

water chestnut: a tasty, nutlike fruit

How Do You Say It?

Ai Mai Un: eye my OON

Aini: EYE nee

Buddhist: BOO dist

Mangsha: MAHNG shah

Sutra: SOO trah

Tai: TIE

Yi Bo: YEE boh

Yi Tan: YEE tahn

Yunnan: you NAHN